MAD ®

Edited by
Albert B. Feldstein

WARNER BOOKS

A Warner Communications Company

Warner Books, Inc.
666 Fifth Avenue
New York, N.Y. 10103

 A Warner Communications Company

Printed in the United States of America

First Printing: February, 1985

10 9 8 7 6 5 4 3 2 1

Combine a dynamic young TV star with the soundtrack of a hot, exploitable singing group and some "R"-rated dialogue, insure it with some sub-plots from other hit films like "Rocky," "American Graffiti," "West Side Story," "Mean Streets," and "Beach Blanket Bingo"...and you've got the formula for one of the biggest block-buster movies of the year, right? Wrong! Because the best "hustle" may not be the one they're dancing up on the screen, but the one foisted on us by the producers—for making millions on a film that does have spectacular choreography...but not much else! Yep, as far as we at MAD are concerned, you wasted your money on . . .

SATURDAY NIGHT FEEBLE

ARTIST: MORT DRUCKER   WRITER: ARNIE KOGEN

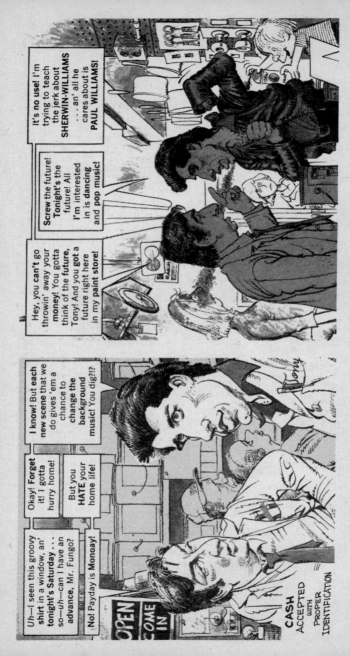

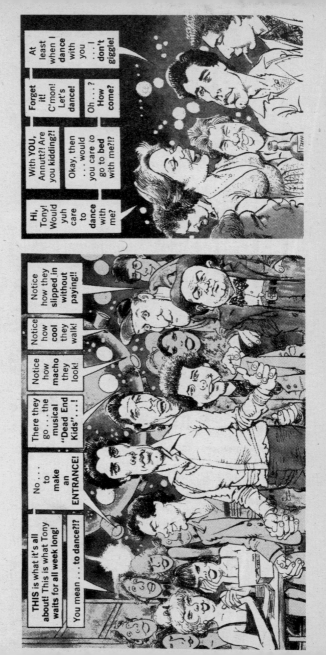

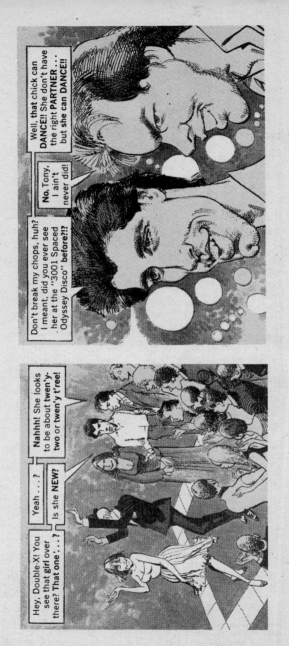

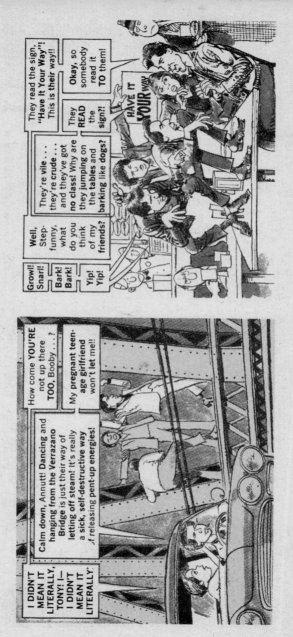

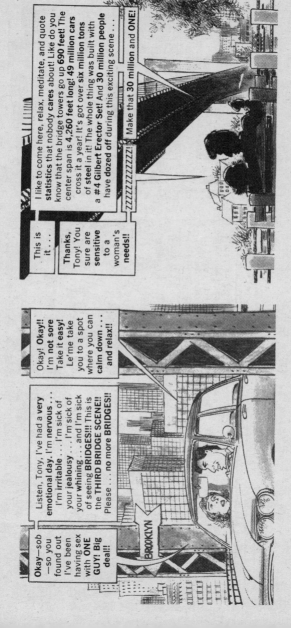

YAAAA!!!!

I've got nothing to live for! I'm short! I'm chicken-hearted! I got my girlfriend pregnant! And on top of that, I'm feeling headachey, listless and out of sorts!

Hey, he's depressed! He's gonna jump! Talk to him, Tony! He'll listen to you!

Hey, Booby . . . did you know that this bridge you are about to jump off has over 300 miles of cable, almost a million yards of concrete, and the water . . . 228 feet below the center span . . . is a chilly 42 degrees! There have been 39 attempted suicides since the bridge was built . . . and of those, three were short people who were also chicken-hearted and had gotten their girlfriends pregnant . . . and—

ONE FRIDAY MORNING

THE LIGHTER SIDE OF...

AIR

AIR

AIR

ARTIST & WRITER:
DAVE BERG

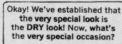

I smell **stale cigarette** smoke! Who's been **smoking**?!

SNIFF SNIFF

I **cannot tell a lie!** It was me!

You?! But **you're** always bragging about how when you **grow up**, you're going to be a **big athlete**!

That's **not** exactly what I **said!** I'm going to be a **FAMOUS** athlete!

How are you going to be **that** when smoking will **stunt your growth**!?!

I'm going to be a **JOCKEY**!!

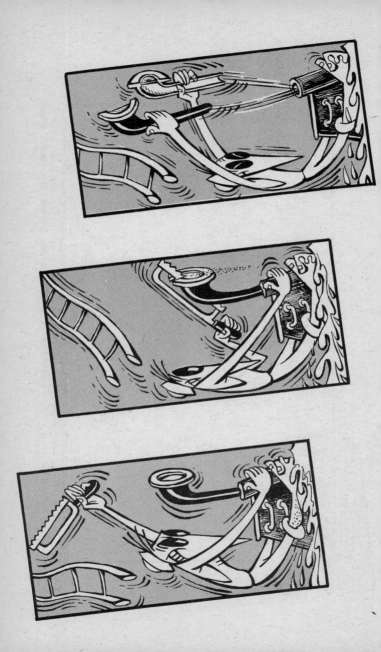

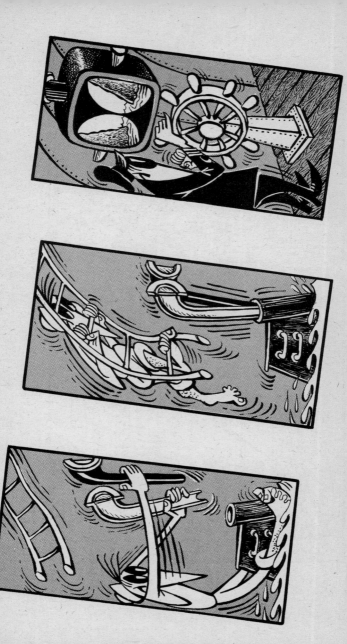

THE MAD

LIKE...
LOVE...
HATE
BOOK

WRITERS: FRANK JACOBS AND MARYLYN IPPOLITO

ARTIST: PAUL COKER, JR.

Don't You LIKE...

. . . your playful
new purebred dog?

Don't You LOVE...

. . . how she frolics
with the other dogs?

Don't You HATE...

. . . trying to dispose of
nine mixed-breed puppies?

Don't You LIKE...

...the surprise of stumbling onto an exotic new restaurant?

Don't You LOVE...

...the surprise of tasting an exotic new Mid-Eastern dish?

Don't You HATE...

...the surprise of waking up at 3 AM with an exotic new heartburn?

Don't You LIKE...

...discovering a new exciting board game?

Don't You LOVE...

... inviting your friends over to play your new game?

Don't You HATE...

... spending the first three hours figuring out the rules?

Don't You LIKE...

... renting a beach house for the summer?

Don't You LOVE...

...the sand...the surf...the sea air...the sun...the sports?

Don't You HATE...

... the uninvited relatives and friends who freeload all summer?

Don't You LIKE...

... sleeping late on your birthday?

Don't You LOVE...

... being served breakfast in bed by your husband and kids?

Don't You HATE...

... having to clean up the mess they made in the kitchen?

Don't You LIKE....

. . . the liberated
age we live in?

Don't You LOVE...

. . . feeling unhibited and free
of the restrictions of society?

Don't You HATE...

. . . being an
unwed mother?

Don't You LIKE...

. . . having a father who is very
interested in your schoolwork?

Don't You LOVE...

. . . conning him into doing
your Math homework for you?

Don't You HATE...

. . . getting a failing mark
on the Math homework he did?

Don't You LIKE...

. . . settling down to watch
Monday Night Football on TV?

Don't You LOVE...

. . . watching your favorite
football team in action?

Don't You HATE...

. . . Cosell telling you you're watching
the poorest-played game in five years?

Don't You LIKE...

... meeting someone
from a foreign country?

Don't You LOVE...

... learning his language so
you can really communicate?

Don't You HATE...

... discovering that
boredom is world-wide?

Don't You LIKE...

... finding the willpower
to stick to your diet?

Don't You LOVE...

... finally losing
twenty-five pounds?

Don't You HATE...

... hearing overweight friends tell
you how scrawny and sickly you look?

Don't You LIKE...

...sitting next to
the school grind?

Don't You LOVE...

... copying his answers
during a Chemistry exam?

Don't You HATE...

... being so stupid you
can't even *copy* correctly?

Don't You LIKE...

. . . going to
Tag Sales?

Don't You LOVE...

. . . picking up a fabulous
floor lamp for only $15.00?

Don't You HATE...

. . . spotting a store unloading
the same lamp for only $9.95?

Don't You LIKE...

... being a worker protected by a Union?

Don't You LOVE...

... your Union leaders demanding and getting you a $10-a-week increase?

Don't You HATE...

... hearing that Management was prepared to go as high as $15?

Don't You LIKE...

...having an Uncle who owns a toy store?

Don't You LOVE...

...when he visits you on your birthday?

Don't You HATE...

...getting a Savings Bond from him as your present?

Hi! I'm Chivy Chaste and you're not! I'll bet you're wondering what a superstar like me is doing here! Well, after my last TV comedy special . . . and it may very well be my last —ha-ha . . . N.B.C. felt that maybe my talent lies in a different direction, like doing interviews! Who knows? If I do good on this assignment for MAD, I might become the male Barbara Walters . . . or, as I used to refer to her on Saturday Night . . . Babwa Wawa! But seriously, folks, I'm here to interview Mr. Cool Carnal, who has been designated as . . .

MAD'S COLLEGE CONCERT COMIC OF THE YEAR

ARTIST: GEORGE WOODBRIDGE   WRITER: LOU SILVERSTONE

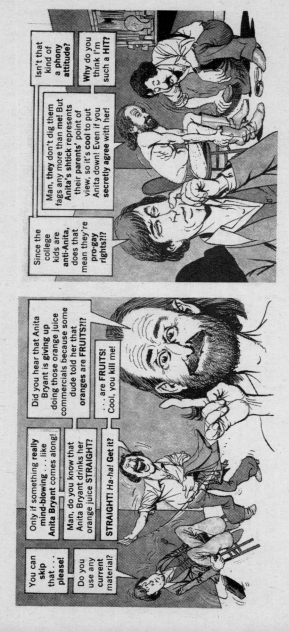

Most young people look forward to the time when they'll be grown up and their parents will stop showering them with the same old trite words of caution, instruction and advice that they've heard almost every day of their lives. Well, forget it! Chances are that when you reach forty, Mom and Dad will still be counseling you to drive slower, dress warmer, and stop hanging out with the wrong crowd. However, there is a way to escape those well-meant parental clichés you've heard a thousand times. The trick is to make your folks realize that their words of "wisdom" are unnecessary, meaningless and downright silly. And to put your point across so you won't get clobbered, MAD furnishes you with tactful examples of

KIDS' FRESH NEW COMEBACKS TO

PARENTS' TIRED OLD COMMENTS

OR "What To Tell Your Parents When They Tell You Not To Do Something You Weren't Going To Do Anyway"

ARTIST: PAUL COKER, JR.   WRITER: TOM KOCH

Don't be late, dear! You know I can't sleep until I hear you come in safe!
Gee, does that mean you stay awake the whole semester while I'm away at college?!

Remember what I told you! Boys don't respect girls who fool around on their first date!
I know, Mom! That's why Harold and I have decided to skip our first date completely . . . and begin tonight with our second!

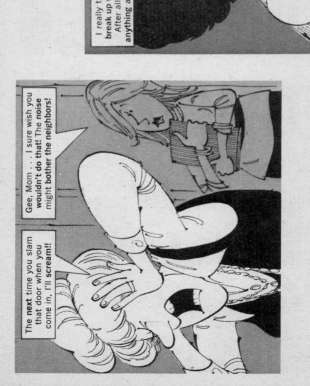

ONE AFTERNOON IN THE POST OFFICE

SOME MAD THINGS WE'LL NEVER UNDER-STAND

ARTIST: JACK RICKARD

WRITER: STAN HART

WE'LL NEVER UNDERSTAND WHY...

. . . a man can get undressed in front
of his wife, and not be embarrassed . . .

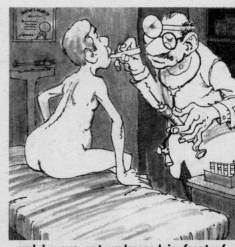

and he can get undressed in front of
his doctor, and not be embarrassed . . .

but he'll be embarrassed when he gets
undressed in front of both of them.

WE'LL NEVER UNDERSTAND WHY...

. . . the State pays $15,000 a year to feed, clothe and house a criminal . . .

while the victim's family gets nothing.

WE'LL NEVER UNDERSTAND WHY...

. . . you leave a measly quarter tip
for the waiter in a luncheonette . . .

who makes as many trips as the waiter
in a fancy restaurant you tip two bucks.

WE'LL NEVER UNDERSTAND WHY...

. . . no matter what city or town you're
driving in when you stop for a light . . .

. . . the guy in the next car
is always picking his nose.

WE'LL NEVER UNDERSTAND WHY...

... you look okay in a regular mirror ...

but you look like hell in a 3-way mirror.

WE'LL NEVER UNDERSTAND WHY...

. . . people who complain about the commercialization of everything . . .

will wear fun tee shirts with commercial messages on them.

WE'LL NEVER UNDERSTAND WHY...

. . . the doctor's nurse will give you a
specific time for an appointment . . .

but when you show up on time, there are
always four or five people ahead of you.

WE'LL NEVER UNDERSTAND WHY...

. . . important letters get lost . . .

while junk mail never does.

WE'LL NEVER UNDERSTAND WHY...

...someone who works hard to become a famous celebrity and be recognized ...

complains bitterly, when she finally makes it, that she has no privacy.

WE'LL NEVER UNDERSTAND WHY...

... the U.S. Government permits the sale of arms to other countries . . .

then sends emissaries all over the world to try and stop the fighting.

WE'LL NEVER UNDERSTAND WHY...

. . . dog and cat lovers hate the
killing of unwanted animals . . .

yet let their dogs and cats run free
to make all those unwanted animals.

WE'LL NEVER UNDERSTAND WHY...

. . . you want your best friend to succeed . . .

. . . but when he does, you feel depressed.

AROUND NOON ON A MOVIE SET

"YOU VILL BUY UR SHTUFF UNDT OU VILL LUFF IT!"

GUE

ONLY VERBOTEN!

<u>TORTURE OF LEARNING DEPT.</u>

Although parents are aware that taxes get higher every year to pay for well equipped schools, kids are equally aware that the quality of school equipment gets lower every year. This doesn't seem plausible, except to those who've browsed through a devilish catalogue that was recently delivered to the MAD office by mistake. It reveals a couple of interesting things about some members of local school boards: (1) They enjoy pocketing a fast buck; (2) They also enjoy grinding spirited children down into docile, obedient nervous wrecks. Sad to say, there's a mailorder firm that happily serves this crowd by replacing education's three R's with its own three S's: Shoddiness, Skulduggery and Sadism. Chances are, you'd probably never learn about this monstrous company unless you stumbled across its secret catalogue, as we did. And since that's not likely to happen accidentally, we'll just show you our copy on purpose, right here and now.

ARTIST: BOB CLARKE   WRITER: TOM KOCH

"TIP-EASY" SCHOOL CHAIRS fool everyone with their deceptively sturdy appearance. Actually, each is hand crafted with a delicate center of balance that can be thrown out of whack with the slightest nudge. You'll want to fill your classrooms with plenty of these beauties to provide shy and clumsy students with a never ending source of embarrassment.

9055—NON-FOLDING CHAIRS THAT FOLD UP ANYWAY
$32.50 ea.

FACTORY REJECT CHALK can be one of your teachers' best weapons in the fight to shatter youthful nerves. Soft texture contains just enough hard chalk lumps to assure one horrifying screech on blackboard before each stick breaks into numerous small pieces. Enjoy watching kids suffer from terrible noise, and then chew them out for wasting chalk.

29551—CRUMMY, CRUMBLY CHALK ....$3.50 doz. boxes

OUT-OF-DATE WORLD GLOBES serve the dual purpose of saving you money while they're making it impossible for your students to pass Geography. Also nice for young nostalgia buffs who prefer to learn about the world as it used to be. These globes are free of defects, and were imported by us from one of the finest map making firms in the Ottoman Empire.

28559—"OLD WORLD" BRAND SCHOOL GLOBES $8.50 ea.

BOTTLED LOCKER ROOM STENCH gives your gym facilities that "lived in" smell. Ideal for newly constructed schools where locker rooms have not yet become sufficiently gamy to make kids throw up when they're required to take Phys. Ed. right after lunch. Also great for confirming the younger generation's expressed belief that the whole world stinks.

11527—ESSENCE OF SWEAT SOCKS $2.75 per 6 oz. can

ENCOURAGE PAPER TOWEL CON-SERVATION in school rest rooms by filling dispensers with our Rough-'N-Ready brand toweling. Cheaply made from semi-raw wood pulp, leaving plenty of splinters and bark particles to dig into tender young skin. You save money as children quickly learn to let hands remain wet, or bring extra handkerchiefs from home.

81442—PAINFUL PAPER TOWELS
29¢ pkg.

WHY DEPEND ON SURPRISE QUIZZES to shatter children's nerves when flickering fluorescent lights in your classrooms can do the job more efficiently? Teachers will love the results as they watch our shoddy fixtures work sub-consciously to turn normally active kids into docile basket cases. Stock up on these factory rejects at special bargain prices.

90268—FAULTY FLICKERING FLU-ORESCENT FIXTURES
$8.75 doz.

INHUMANLY COLD SHOWER lets you provide an agonizing climax to gym classes that are not quite as unpleasant as you'd like to make them. Patented device filters out all hot and luke warm water to make compulsory showers a chilling experience. Guaranteed to separate the men from the boys, assuming you've already separated the boys from the girls prior to showering.

36471—"ARCTIC KNIGHT" BRAND GYM SHOWERS
$11,500 per dozen units

GENUINE ALGAE SLIME-AND-GLYCERINE FLOOR POLISH creates an amazing slick surface that prevents boisterous youngsters from running in school hallways. Also prevents less boisterous youngsters from walking in school hallways. Order several cans to polish up your crummy floors while you polish off your crummy students.

4846—UPSY-DAISY FLOOR POL-ISH .... $3.50 gallon

LOPSIDED BLADE ACTION lets this deluxe classroom sharpener chew up entire pencils without ever producing a usable point. A real money maker for school systems that sell pencils to students at a whopping mark-up over cost. Loud grinding noise is also good for disrupting studies.
23354—"LONG, HARD GRIND" BRAND SHARPENER. $4.98

"QUICK CHANGE" COMBINATION LOCK assures punishable tardiness when installed on student lockers. New improved model looks like an ordinary lock. But miraculously, the same combination never works twice to open it. Kids eventually give up hope, allowing school janitors to collect valuable personal belongings when they open locks with hack saws during summer vacation.
77351—"LOCK NESS MONSTER" BRAND LOCKS....... $14.50 doz.

"SONGS AMERICAN CHILDREN HATE." This amazing book includes the hundred least loved ballads of today's grade schoolers. Features all verses of such draggy numbers as "Flow Gently, Sweet Afton" and "Beautiful Dreamer." Guaranteed to turn kids away from music for life, and encourage them to devote full attention to the more profitable fine arts, such as computer programming.
8853—"OLDIES BUT BADDIES" SONG BOOK **$5.95**

ROLL DOWN-SNAP UP WALL MAP enables teachers to win the undivided attention of young day dreamers. Hair trigger roller mechanism recoils with a startling racket at the slightest touch of instructor's pointer. Maps of all continents available except Australia, which is too small to make enough noise.
19005—ATTENTION GETTER WALL MAPS .... **$14.50 ea.**

**VISITING THE SCHOOL NURSE BE-
COMES A MEMORABLE EXPERI-
ENCE,** once you equip her office
with a prominent display of our
frightening veterinary hypodermic
needles. Watch young malingerers
and hypochondriacs recover quickly, assuming your staff never tells
them that the needles are really designed for tranquilizing elephants.
**91117—SURE CURE HYPODER-
MICS** .... **$2.60 ea.**

DEFECTIVE M. & M. BRAND CRAYONS
melt in your mouth and in your hand.
Use of too much paraffin and watery dye
in manufacturing this batch makes crayons become gooey soft when exposed to
temperatures above 35 degrees. A dou-
ble-barreled horror for kids as they get
yelled at by teachers for ruining their art
work, and then get yelled at by parents
for ruining their clothes.
**5569—VIVID COLOR-LIVID REACTION
CRAYONS** .... **43¢ box**

**SILENCE ANNOYING SQUEALS OF EX-
CITEMENT** in your schoolyard during re-
cess by providing children with one of
our defective, deflated playground balls.
Squeal provoking games are utterly impossible with these lifeless babies, forcing kids to schloomp around in blessed,
sullen silence. Order several. You'll be
pleased with the results.
**11528—DEAD, SQUOOSHY PLAY-
GROUND BALL** .... **$1.75 ea.**

**DELUXE TWO-SPEED DRINKING FOUN-
TAIN** is specially designed for educa-
tional purposes. Secret setting can be
changed in a jiffy from ''Feeble Drip'' to
''Soaking Splash.'' Helps gullible pri-
mary graders learn never to take anything for granted in life. Also helps teach
desert survival techniques by forcing
kids to go through entire school day
without drinkable water.
**2791—DRENCH-OR-DRIBBLE DRINK-
ING FOUNTAIN** **$129.95**

SCARY CLASSROOM ANIMALS enable youngsters to learn the meaning of fear while they're also learning the meaning of zoology. Why settle for insipid hamsters or white mice when iguanas and boa constrictors are hardier species better able to take care of themselves over week-ends and vacations?

8842—VICIOUS BEASTS (ASSORTED TYPES AND SIZES)

$15 ea.

CHINTZY, ILL FITTING COSTUMES can add a note of comedy to otherwise boring school pageants. We found these at a rummage sale in Taiwan, and pass the savings on to you. Costumes feature cheap material, poor sewing and inaccurately marked sizes to assure you that kids will make fools of themselves on stage, and turn your next dull pageant into a laugh riot.

877—LOUSY LINCOLN COSTUME $6.65
878—PUNK PILGRIM COSTUME . $6.85
879—CRUDDY XMAS COSTUME . .$7.29

MADDENING MIMEO MACHINE lowers student grade averages by cleverly smudging key words in quiz questions. Mechanism is equipped with irregular ink dribbler, automatic stencil ripper, cockeyed paper feeder and other illegibility devices not normally found on mimeos in this price range.

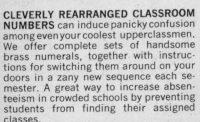

26465—SMUDGY MIMEO **$47.50**

CLEVERLY REARRANGED CLASSROOM NUMBERS can induce panicky confusion among even your coolest upperclassmen. We offer complete sets of handsome brass numerals, together with instructions for switching them around on your doors in a zany new sequence each semester. A great way to increase absenteeism in crowded schools by preventing students from finding their assigned classes.

33917—CLASSY BRASSY CLASSROOM NUMBERS..............**$42 per 10**

PRECISION WEATHER INSTRUMENT WITH ELECTRIC BELL ATTACHMENT automatically sounds alarm for school fire drill whenever temperature drops to zero or wind reaches 40 M.P.H. Completely eliminates risk of staging drills on nice warm days when children might actually enjoy going outdoors.

5578—CLANG-A-MATIC, PNEUMONIA-MATIC FIRE DRILL TIMER $49.95

INFERIOR SHOP TOOLS doom junior high school woodworking projects to botched up disaster from the word go. Helps youngsters learn to accept the agony of defeat as they struggle in vain to make bookends, etc. Tool defects are scarcely noticeable, causing kids to accept teacher's judgment that their own klutziness is responsible for lousy results.

33014—CROOKED TOOTH SAW $8.50
33015—NICKED BLADE PLANE $7.75

WEIRDLY MARKED LAB EQUIPMENT helps turn even the simplest chemistry experiment into a student's nightmare. These test tubes were picked up cheap in a small European country that still uses such quaint measurements as hogsheads, gills and pennyweights. Impossibility of translating lab results into commonly used terms enables teachers to base final grades on pure whim.

6877—ODDBALL TEST TUBES 26¢ ea.

OUT-OF-FOCUS SLIDE PROJECTOR makes all pictures look alike, thereby ending wasteful expense of buying new slides for new lectures. Poor lens quality coupled with non-functioning focus dial permit you to identify shapeless blobs on screen as anything you wish. Comes complete with "Scenic Italy" slide set for illustrating talks on biology, safe driving or even scenic Italy.

11519—G.A.F. (GOOD AND FUZZY) BRAND PROJECTOR $79.75

ESTABLISHMENT ANGUISH DEPT.

When Radicals first climbed up on their soap boxes in our Grandparents' day to denounce "The System," they ranted mostly against Big Banks and Heartless Corporations that tromped on Impoverished Working People. By the Hippie Era, of the '60's, orators had broadened their definition of "The System" to embrace the Federal Government, the Local Police, the California Lettuce Growers and anybody else who wore shoes. By then, the victims included not only Impoverished Working People, but also impoverished people who wouldn't dream of working. Today, we are beginning to realize that "The System" has become even bigger and more ominous than we were previously told. Today, it includes every computer-crazed clerk, every pompous planner, every bungling bureaucrat, every managerial misfit and every inflexible imbecile whose crackpot concepts are waiting to snare us all in a web of cockeyed conformity. In short, "The System" has grown from a Left-Winger's Pet Peeve to a Man-Eating Monster. But no matter how much it may have changed over the years, there's only one comment you can make about it that's as true today as it was then, namely

YOU CAN'T BEAT THE SYSTEM

ARTIST: JACK DAVIS   WRITER: TOM KOCH

YOU CAN'T BEAT THE SYSTEM, BECAUSE...

... banks only give free TV sets to people who open $10,000 Savings Accounts ... which automatically excludes people who could really use free TV sets.

YOU CAN'T BEAT THE SYSTEM, BECAUSE...

... there's seldom an opportunity to vote for an honest politician in the general elections because so few of them can raise enough campaign money to win in the primaries.

YOU CAN'T BEAT THE SYSTEM, BECAUSE...

...TV shows always wait until the very end to announce that you've been watching the first half of a two-part program, just so they can trap you into wasting another whole hour next week.

YOU CAN'T BEAT THE SYSTEM, BECAUSE...

...most innoculations discovered by medical science to protect you against deadly disease have side effects that kill you even faster.

YOU CAN'T BEAT THE SYSTEM, BECAUSE...

. . . Child Labor Laws prevent your kids from going to work and contributing to the family income until they're old enough to leave home and continue not contributing to the family income.

YOU CAN'T BEAT THE SYSTEM, BECAUSE...

. . . your creditors will keep on charging you 18% interest on the money you don't really owe, while you're trying to prove that you don't even owe it.

YOU CAN'T BEAT THE SYSTEM, BECAUSE...

. . . waiting for department stores to have sales merely assures you of a wide selection of all that atrocious junk that they couldn't get rid of at regular prices.

YOU CAN'T BEAT THE SYSTEM, BECAUSE...

. . . there's no way to land a job without having previous experience . . . which you can only get by holding a job . . . which you can't land unless you have previous experience.

YOU CAN'T BEAT THE SYSTEM, BECAUSE...

... bureaucrats always make you file a complaint form
to report that they've misplaced one of your other forms,
... and then they promptly misplace your complaint form.

YOU CAN'T BEAT THE SYSTEM, BECAUSE...

... it's only your questionable word against the phone company's
infallible computer when you claim you didn't make 5 calls to the
recorded voice in Perth, Australia, that gives the correct time.

YOU CAN'T BEAT THE SYSTEM, BECAUSE...

. . . anyone who's sick enough to need a prescription drug is obviously in no condition to figure out how to open one of those "child-proof" medicine bottles.

YOU CAN'T BEAT THE SYSTEM, BECAUSE...

. . . the only time you're allowed to park your car within walking distance of most stores is when they're closed.

YOU CAN'T BEAT THE SYSTEM, BECAUSE...

. . . saving money by patronizing a self-service gas station means that nobody ever checks your radiator, which means you're sure to burn up your engine, which means you really aren't saving money.

YOU CAN'T BEAT THE SYSTEM, BECAUSE...

. . . all cars are carefully designed to make it impossible for a mechanic to repair one part without breaking at least two others.

YOU CAN'T BEAT THE SYSTEM, BECAUSE...

...it's impossible to survive a hospital's endless admitting procedure unless you have the wisdom to check in before you get sick.

YOU CAN'T BEAT THE SYSTEM, BECAUSE...

...camping out all night to be the first in line for tickets to a David Bowie concert only means you'll probably be mugged and robbed of your ticket money before the box office opens.

... the only thing going up faster than the price of gasoline is the national crime rate, which means that when you have to start riding a bicycle to work, it will immediately be stolen.

YOU CAN'T BEAT THE SYSTEM, BECAUSE...

BLAP

SOLD!

... appliance warranties never go into effect until you sign a card stating that everything that's likely to go wrong will be your fault.

ADOLESSONS DEPT.

So you just reached your 13th birthday, and you think that automatically makes you a Teenager, right? Wrong! Sure, you're a Teenager chronologically, and naturally you are going through physical and psychological changes (if you're a boy your voice is changing from high to deep; if you're a girl, your voice is changing from no to yes). But like most other careers (and make no mistake about it, you are embarking on a 7 year career), Teenaging requires careful training. And so, to help pave the way for you, the following publication contains everything you will ever have to know about the highly complex, but deeply rewarding art of

HOW TO
TEENAGE

ARTIST: GEORGE WOODBRIDGE   WRITER: LARRY SIEGEL

THE TEENAGE IMAGE

To begin with, it is absolutely imperative to project the right image. And here the catchword is hostility. Remember, a Teenager is *always* hostile. On the outside chance that you're a Teenage Freak (i.e., a member of the one percentile in the Teenage World who is a pleasant person) don't worry about it; you'll just have to try harder and work on your hostility. One of the best ways to wipe those obnoxious pleasant thoughts from your mind and become angry is to think of terrible things. For example, oil tycoons, environment polluters, Adolf Hitler. If this doesn't work, think of your parents. That *never* fails.

So much for your inner being. Now for your outer appearance. The same way that you learned the three R's in school, you must learn the three S's of Teenaging. These are: Sulking, Slouching, and Schlumping.

The Teenage Sulk

The ever-popular sulk is easy to master once you get the hang of it. Close your eyes almost all the way until they are slits, dilate your nostrils, and let the corners of your mouth droop until they reach your chin. Got it? Good. Now freeze this expression for seven years.

The Teenage Slouch

Correct posture is imperative in Teenaging. Take a jacket off a hanger in the closet, put it on, go in the street, and practice moving along with your shoulders hunched over so that you look like a walking question mark. Note: if you find your back tends to straighten up uncontrollably from time to time, leave the hanger *in* the jacket.

The Teenage Schlump

Schlumping is not only a way of life for Teenagers, but also a highly polished art form. As illustrated here, the proper schlump is not quite lying down, but a little bit more than sitting. The successfully schlumping Teenager can flop around like this for weeks at a time.

Historical note: The most unusual case of schlumping occurred in 1974 in Lincoln, Nebraska, when 16-year-old Alex Gribbish made the "Guinness Book of Records" and "Believe It Or Not" in the same year, having schlumped for 109 straight days, and then dying and coming back to earth as a beer pretzel.

GROOMING AND DRESS

As a Teenager, you should know immediately that the most important part of your body is your hair (of course there *is* one other part of your body, which *may* be as important and *might* give you as much pleasure, but we'll discuss your ears later when we get to Rock Music and Telephoning).

You have a choice of wearing your hair one of three ways: on your shoulders, on your waist, or around your ankles. For girls, it's pretty much the same. There has been some experimentation in recent years, whereby the hair is worn on a revolutionary place—the head. One of the most common of these styles is called the Afro. And it's become so popular of late that even some Black teenagers are trying it.

As far as dress is concerned, you have a choice of two shirts—the monogrammed T-shirt and the work shirt. If you wear the latter, you'll find you'll become very popular if you wear it unbuttoned to the waist (particularly if you're a girl).

We now come to *the* most important article of attire for Teenagers—the jeans. There's only one thing you really have to know about jeans: *they must be tight*. If you try on a size 28 waist and you find you can't breathe, do the sensible thing: get a size 26.

Now let's try a little quiz. Which Teenager in the following illustration is wearing jeans, and which one isn't?

Answer: You got it right away, didn't you? Of course. The Teenager on the left is wearing tight French jeans and the nude Teenager on the right has a bad skin condition.

In case there is ever any doubt in your mind about jeans, remember this simple slogan: "If you can sit, the pants don't fit."

TEENAGE COMMUNICATION

As a Teenager it's vital that you learn how to communicate with others.

If you feel upset or emotional, don't be afraid to display your feelings. Sigh a lot, moan pitiously, fling your arms around, use grandiose gestures, be dramatic (think of Shakespeare's King Lear).

While at other times, you may want things from your parents. The best way in which to communicate this is by snorting, grunting, growling and beating on your chest (think of Dino De Laurentiis's King Kong).

As a last resort (and remember, *only* as a last resort) you may have to speak. The important thing is: don't panic. But before you utter a syllable, remember this: Teenagers are always incoherent. The best way to achieve this effect is by swallowing your words. Does this worry you? It shouldn't. Medical science has proved time and time again that Teenagers can eat *anything*. Following are some typical garbled Teenage speeches and their closest English translations. Use them. Perhaps you might even want to make up a few of your own:

TYPICAL TEENAGE COMMENTS	CLOSEST ENGLISH TRANSLATION
(a) Psspazzdebuu.	(a) Please pass the butter.
(b) Lezzgoroconceshrotuez.	(b) Let's go to the rock concert on Shrove Tuesday.
(c) Mizzstorkahwanpotpotpot.	(c) Mr. Storekeeper, I want a potted plant, French Fries and marijuana.
(d) Sicksexsax.	(d) I'm tired of making out with saxophonists.
(e) Ackneenonu.	(e) I've had this bad complexion for years.
(f) Brtzzglgfrppquint.	(f) Brtzzglgfrppquint.

TEENAGING
AND THE TELEPHONE

The two main things to know about telephoning are these: if you're a boy it's all relatively simple. You dial a friend, you say, "Heymayawangobowg?" (Hey man, you want to go bowling?) Your friend says yes; you say, "Meetchoncor," (I'll meet you on the corner) and that's it.

For a Teenager girl, however, it's a whole different ball game. Whenever you're home, the telephone *must* be permanently attached to your ear. This is not always easy, and for that reason science is working overtime to help you in this area. For instance, at present in Terre Haute, Indiana, an inventor is working on a project, whereby if you pierce extra large holes in your ear-lobes, you may slip the telephone wire through. As soon as he irons out one last bug—namely, how to push the phone receiver through the ear-lobe first—it should be on the market.

Remember, it doesn't really matter what you say on the phone, *just don't hang up.* Important note: you must—repeat, *must* call up the girl friend you just spent the day with, no later than three minutes after you leave her. It is vital that she know about your fascinating trip home—across the street; the incredible experience of opening your front door; and your near brush with death walking through the garbage-littered mine-field of your room.

In short, the telephone is not only an integral part of your life, it's also an inseparable part of your body. And you will learn, in time, under ordinary circumstances, how to keep it on your ear at all times. Occasionally, however, an emergency situation may come up. Here is only one typical example, and how to handle it.

In the event of fire, cradle the phone on your right shoulder. Hold the fire extinguisher tank in your left hand and hold the hose in your right. Then spray the fire and talk to your girl friend at the same time. Note: In case of extreme emergency, like a cramp in your shoulder, do the only sensible thing: drop the fire extinguisher.

TEENAGING AND MUSIC

There is really nothing anybody has to tell a Teenager about music. All your actions in this area will be instinctive. You will instinctively know what stereo to buy, where to install your 83 speakers, what records to get. And then after an evening of listening to rock, you will instinctively know how to relax in front of your TV set watching "The 11:00 O'Clock News for Viewers with Impaired Hearing."

Instead let's discuss music-performance. For argument's sake, let's say that you have just reached 13 and you haven't cut a record yet (this has been known to happen in one out of every 200,000 births). The first thing you'll want to do is form your own Rock Group. Now let's try another little quiz. Which of the following Teenagers should you use in your Group?

Answer: Forget the guy on the left. He seems to know how to *read* music, which could be a lot of trouble in Rock. Ignore the guy in the center. He is standing too still and is not shaking his body. Choose the guy on the right. If nothing else, at least he *looks* like a Rock Singer.

Once the Group is formed, you will want to choose a title. Stay away from the following names, which have already been used by successful Rock Groups: Kiss, Chicago, Queen, Boston, Eagles. Here are some suggestions: Bronchitis, Phlegm, Belch, Canarsie, Puke, and Bellybutton. (Note: Use only *one* of these names, not all of them; since this happens to be the title of a Teenage Law Firm in Mamaroneck, N.Y.).

Finally, let's say you have a beautiful singing voice and have won music awards in school. This need not be a problem if you work on it. Just remember that to be a successful Rock Singer today, no matter how old you are, or what part of the country or world you come from—you *must* sound like the constipated driver of a poultry truck in Yazoo, Mississippi.

TEENAGING AND SEX

First of all, let's put an end to a popular myth. We object to the ridiculous claim that most young people nowadays make out for the first time when they are Teenagers. This is a flagrant lie. It's true, of course, that a large number of 13-year-olds *do* make out, but believe us, it's not for the first time.

We suppose we're a bit old-fashioned in this matter, but concerning sex, we advise caution at all times. Naturally you're going to meet people you like and you're going to want to start dating. That's perfectly normal. Just take your time, get to know the other person, spend months building up a relationship and developing mutual interests. And then—and *only* then—is it time to pop the first important question. Namely, "Are you a boy or a girl?"

Considering the way Teenagers look and dress nowadays (see above illustration) it's natural for you to be confused. You just don't know. This need not be a problem. The problem arises when the person you ask doesn't know either.

As soon as you both find out, and you're delighted to discover that you're a boy and she's a girl, or vice-versa, or vice-vice, or versa-versa, proceed accordingly. (See Chapter 24, "Once In A While It's Not So Terrible To Fool Mother Nature").

If your relationship develops into something permanent, you might want to look more deeply into such interesting areas as Chapter 25 ("Sex Before The Wedding") Chapter 26 ("Sex After The Wedding") and perhaps the most interesting area of them all, Chapter 27 ("Sex *During* the Wedding").

TEENAGING MISCELLANIA

In our concluding chapter we will try to cover briefly a few other important areas of Teenaging.

Handling Weirdos

If you ever walk into your house and are suddenly and unexpectedly accosted by an elderly stranger, don't panic or call the police. Distract him by introducing yourself and starting up a conversation. Who knows, in time you may even get to like your Father.

Earning Extra Money

Teenagers can always use a few extra dollars. You can look into a part-time job, if you wish. But there is a simpler way: apply for Federal Funds. This is not nearly as difficult as it may sound. Merely wire Pres. Carter and have him declare your room a Disaster Area.

Teenaging And Religion

You may want to consider joining the thousands of other Teenagers who are turning to Religion lately and are beginning to see the light. You find this hard to believe? Only last week 15-year-old Rick Hammerfleisch, of Los Angeles, received a sermon from the Mount and saw a man walking on water. His explanation for these phenomena was both simple and reverent: There's no skiing this weekend, but surf's up.

Finally, we would like to close with a multiple-choice quiz.

Why is this typical Teenager watching "The Six Million Dollar Man" with one eye, while reading a book with the other, as he listens to a Stevie Wonder record and a football game with one ear, while talking on the phone with his mouth and listening with his other ear?

(a) He is practicing to join a Circus Side Show as a Mental Wizard
(b) He is rehearsing to go on "The Gong Show" as a One-Man Concentration Machine.
(c) None of these.

Answer: (c) None of these. He is studying for a Geometry final.

THE SHAPE OF ZINGS TO COME

A MAD LOOK AT...

MISHAPS OF

THE FUTURE

ARTIST & WRITER: PAUL PETER PORGES

RECALL OF ALL MEDIUM-PRICED GYROCARS BY MANUFACTURER

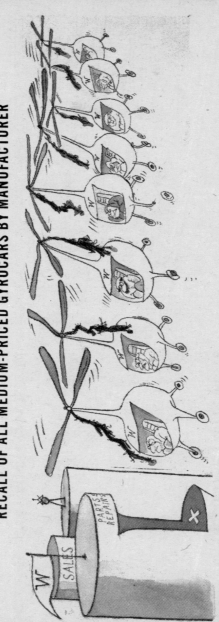

DELAY ON THE 8:36 A.M. PEOPLE-MOVER

LASER BEAM LEAK

OUTER SPACE WASTE-DISPOSAL FALL-OUT

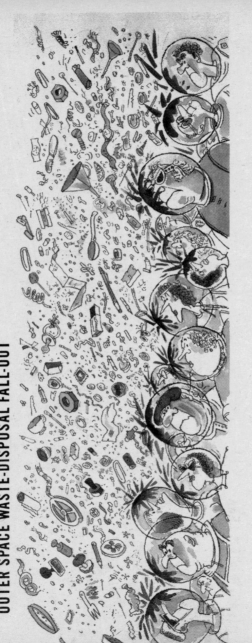

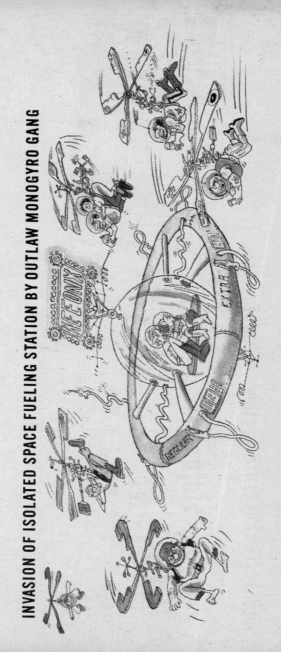

WILDCAT STRIKE BY CENTRAL COMPUTER DATA TERMINALS

GRAFFITI VANDALISM OF INTERHABITAT RAPID MONORAIL

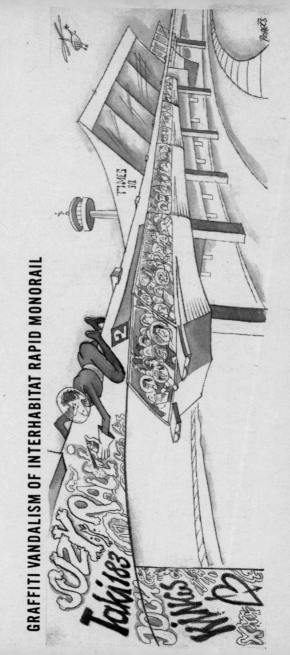

MISMATCH OF REPLACEMENT STRIPS TO OUT-OF-STYLE ORIGINAL ARTIFICIAL LAWN TURF

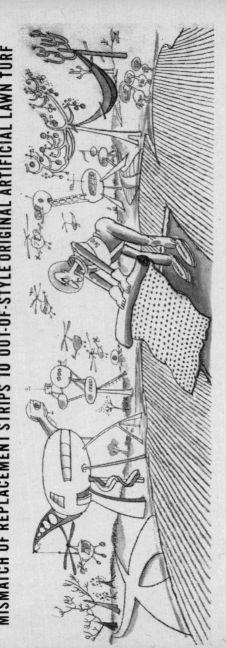

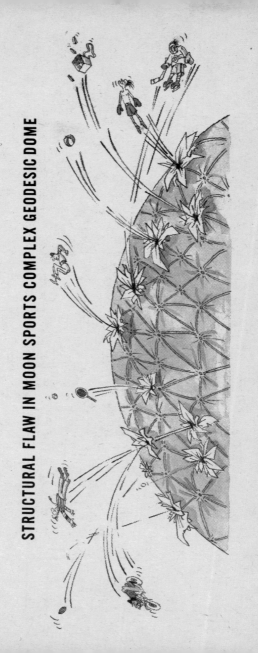

STRUCTURAL FLAW IN MOON SPORTS COMPLEX GEODESIC DOME

TECHNICAL BREAKDOWN OF PEOPLE-RECYCLING PLANT

HOW CAN YOU TRUST...

ARTIST: PAUL COKER, JR.   WRITER: PAUL PETER PORGES

... The Druggist who does both urine analysis ... and sundaes!

... the Wildlife Guide who is covered with poison ivy sores!

. . . the law-and-order Mayor who double-parks his imported $28,000 official car!

. . . The Ecologist who litters the streets with his pamphlets urging us to save our pulp woods!

... the Airline pilot whose pre-flight check consists of kicking the tires, and who hangs a rabbit's foot on his instrument panel!

... the Investment Expert who brown bags his lunch, and wears 1960 type narrow ties and shoes that need re-soling!

. . . the exclusive Men's Shop Clerk who wears a dark blue suit with brown shoes and white anklet socks!

. . . the Suicide-Prevention Line that's always busy!

. . . the Little League Coach who has 3 sons,
4 nephews and his kid sister on the team!

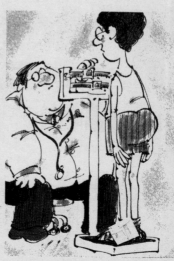

. . . the Diet Doctor who weighs over
300 pounds and wheezes when he talks!

THE LIGHTER

N

Just **look** at this meal! Everything is **harmful**! The **sugar** is **poison** . . . the **salt** is bad for high **blood pressure** . . . the **bread** has no nutrition!

Oh-oh! The **Health Nut** is at it again!

Yeah! Knock it **off** and let us **eat**!

The **milk** has **radiation fall-out** . . . the **butter, eggs** and **meat** have **artery-clogging cholestero** . . . the **fruits** and **vegetables** ar poisoned by **chemical sprays** . . the **fish** has traces of **mercury**—

10-4, Good Buddy! This is **Night Rider** saying "Happy numbers to you!" and going **10-7!**

MUST you play with that **toy** every time we go for an evening drive?!?

Toy? **TOY?** This is an **expensive, high-technology CB Radio** . . . not a **plaything!** It's a modern method of **communicating messages** between **moving vehicles** that was **originally** developed by **professional drivers,** but has **now** come into **general use!**

What, may I ask, do **you** do for a living?

You know **very well** that I'm a **Harvard graduate,** that I'm a **Corporate Lawyer** earning an income in **six figures!!**

So **WHY** are you **playing** at being a **TRUCK DRIVER?!**

Every night, it's the same thing! All you do is **watch** TV for **five** or **six hours!!**

And **what** do you watch?!? **Crime** shows! **War** shows! **Heartbreaking** drama shows! **World** catastrophe shows! Don't you ever get **sick** of that junk?! Why don't you **shut the damn set off** already?!?

Okay! **Okay!** I'll shut it off right after **The Eleven O'Clock News!**

Why do you want to watch the **News?!?**

It'll just be a re-hash of the **depressing stuff** you **already saw** on all those **other** shows!!

EARLY ONE MORNING IN SOUTH AMERICA

Today, there are women Governors, members of Congress, newscasters, executives, West Point cadets, etc. Women have a brand new image everywhere . . . except in the world of TV Sitcom Shows, where they apparently never heard of Women's Lib. There, women are still portrayed as sex symbols or brainless dolts or helpless clods or man-hungry idiots. This is especially true of the hit show about two female brewery workers who are all of the above . . . except sex symbols! Namely:

Lavoine & Shoiley

ARTIST: ANGELO TORRES   WRITER: LOU SILVERSTONE

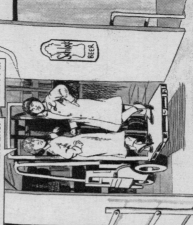

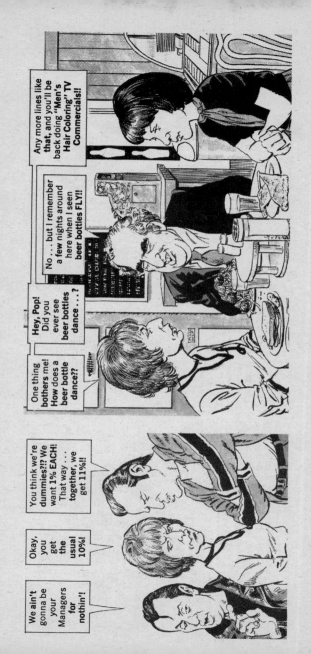

We'll spread a rumor that Lavoine and Shoiley are . . . y'know . . . EASY! An' the Judges will vote for 'em, figurin' that they'll get a little—uh—reward!
Does the reward come out of our 11%?!?

We'll leave a message here in the Executive Washroom, where the Contest Judges can't miss it . . . !
LAVOINE AND SHOILEY ARE PUSHOVERS! THEY NEVER SAY NO!
I just learned a very important lesson, Loonie! Executives go to bathrooms just like ordinary workers! That could only happen in the good ol' U.S.A.!!
Boy, wait till the Judges read this . . . !
Hey! Where're YOU goin'?!?
I'm going' to see Lavoine an' Shoiley!
I just read that they're "PUSHOVERS"!

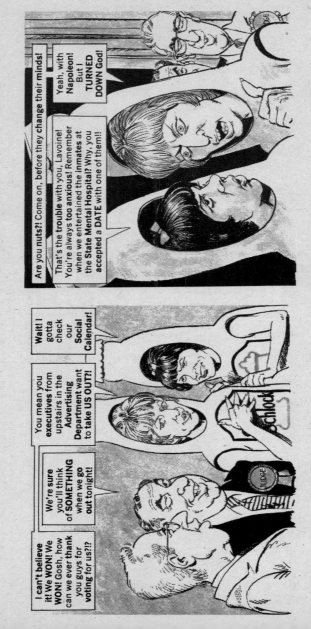

Hey, you guys! We changed our minds!

Hey, fellas! Wait for us!!

. . . and did your Aunt Mary Margaret's "Mr. Right" come along?

Not yet! But she's still waiting! That woman's been waiting for forty long years!

FORTY YEARS?!?

Lavoine, you know why we get into these situations? We never think of anything but men!

From now on, we have to be more selective! It's like my Aunt Mary Margaret always said! "If you wait long enough, Mr. Right will come along!"

What else is there?